# SETH LAKEMAN
## FREEDOM FIELDS

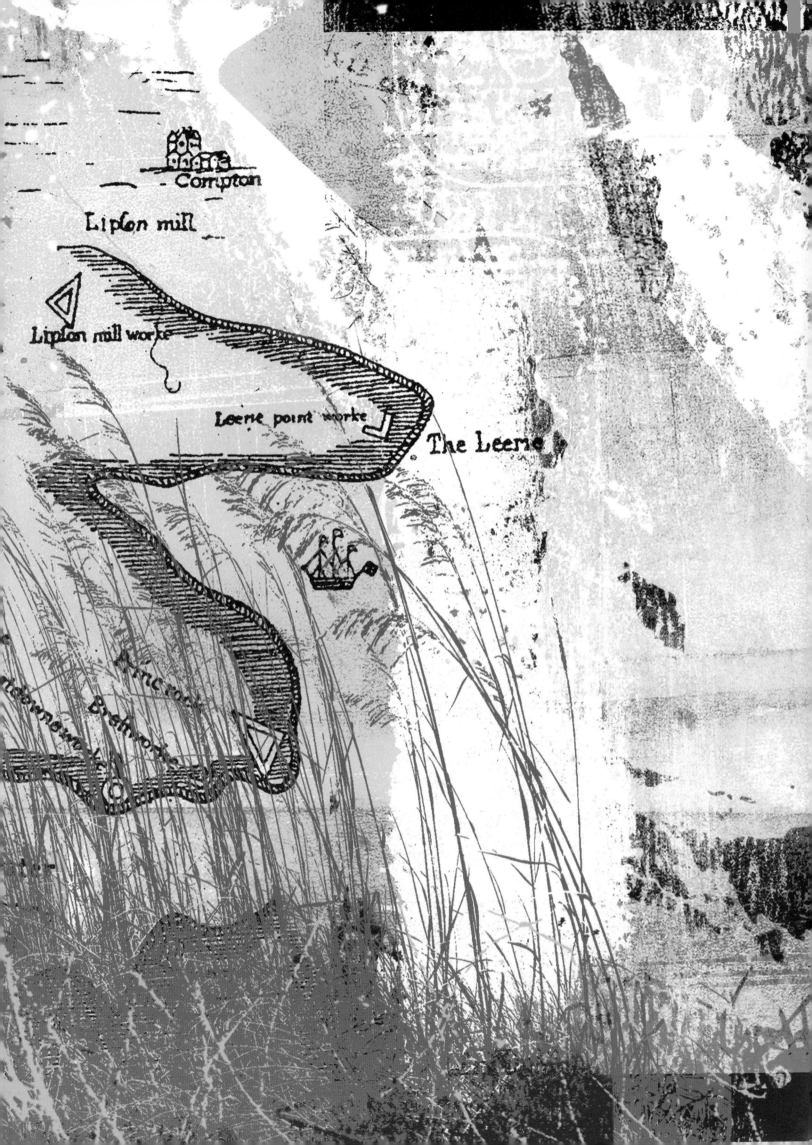

Compton

Lipſon mill

Lipſon mill workes

Leeſne point workes

The Leeſne

© 2006 by International Music Publications Ltd
First published by International Music Publications Ltd in 2006
International Music Publications Ltd is a Faber Music company
3 Queen Square, London WC1N 3AU

Arranged by Alex Davis & Tom Fleming
Engraved by Camden Music
Edited by Lucy Holliday & Olly Weeks

Photography by Derrick Santini
Design & Art Direction by Fury
Cover Illustration by Tim Marrs

Printed in England by Caligraving Ltd

ISBN10: 0-571-52752-3
EAN13: 978-0-571-52752-6

To buy Faber Music publications or to find out about the full range
of titles available, please contact your local music retailer
or Faber Music sales enquiries:

Faber Music Ltd, Burnt Mill, Elizabeth Way, Harlow, CM20 2HX England
Tel: +44(0)1279 82 89 82 Fax: +44(0)1279 82 89 83
sales@fabermusic.com fabermusic.com

Inspired by a Cornish shipwreck in 1780 at Silver Dollar Bay. People still dig for her treasure.

# LADY OF THE SEA

## Words and Music by Seth Lakeman

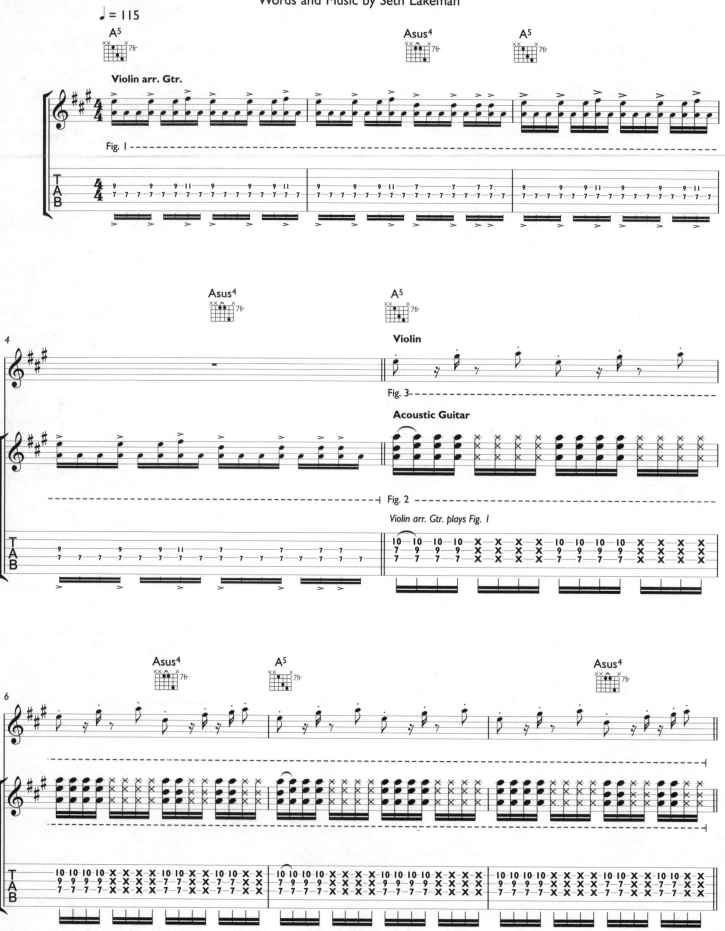

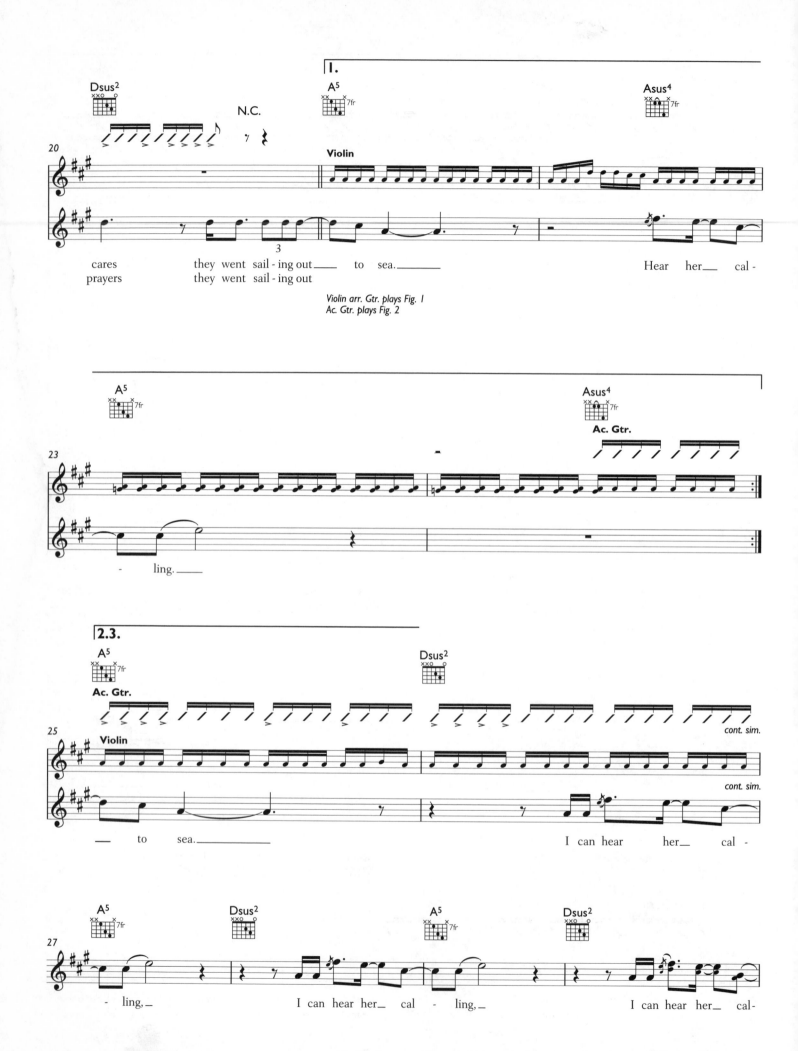

*A young man is haunted by
the lover he mistook for a swan.*

# SETTING OF THE SUN

## Words and Music by Seth Lakeman

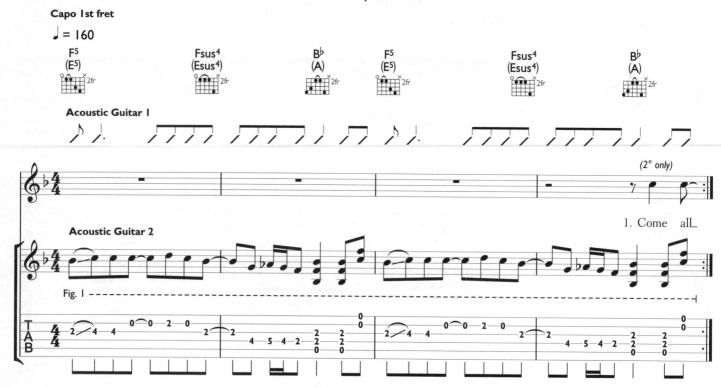

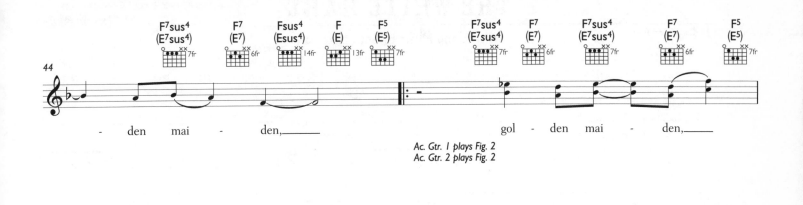

-den mai - den,_____ gol - den mai - den,_____

Ac. Gtr. 1 plays Fig. 2
Ac. Gtr. 2 plays Fig. 2

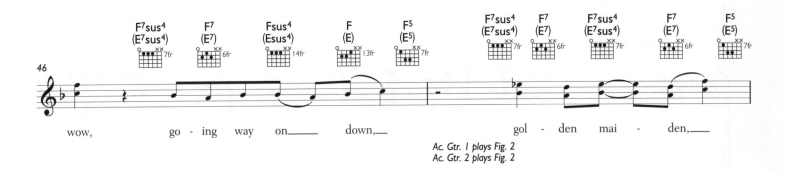

wow, go - ing way on_____ down,_____ gol - den mai - den,_____

Ac. Gtr. 1 plays Fig. 2
Ac. Gtr. 2 plays Fig. 2

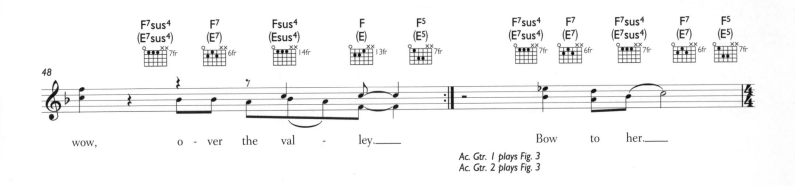

wow, o - ver the val - ley._____ Bow to her._____

Ac. Gtr. 1 plays Fig. 3
Ac. Gtr. 2 plays Fig. 3

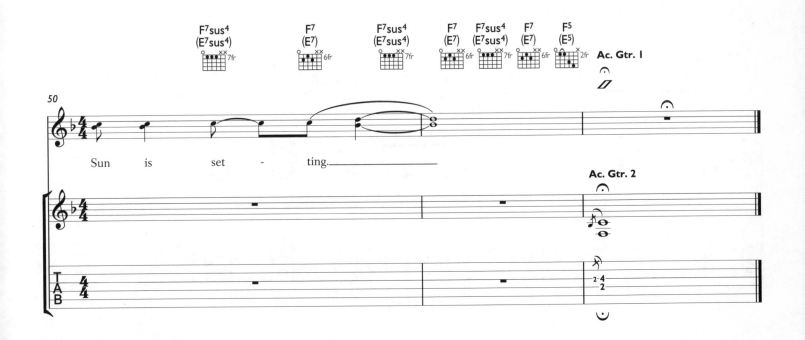

Sun is set - ting._____

# THE WHITE HARE

Words and Music by Seth Lakeman

*A westcountry legend that tells of a witch who takes the form of a white hare and goes out looking for prey at night. If she catches your eye she steals your soul away.*

**Capo 3rd fret**

♩ = 135

1. I heard her in the

2. Out u - pon the - ling you.
3. If you go___

(Ooh.___ La la la.___

(Ooh.)___

# THE COLLIERS

Words and Music by Seth Lakeman

*Based upon a true story at Gresford Colliery of one of the worst mining disasters of the 20th Century.*

**Capo 1st fret**

**Tune guitar:**
① = D ④ = D
② = A ⑤ = A
③ = G ⑥ = D (lowest string)

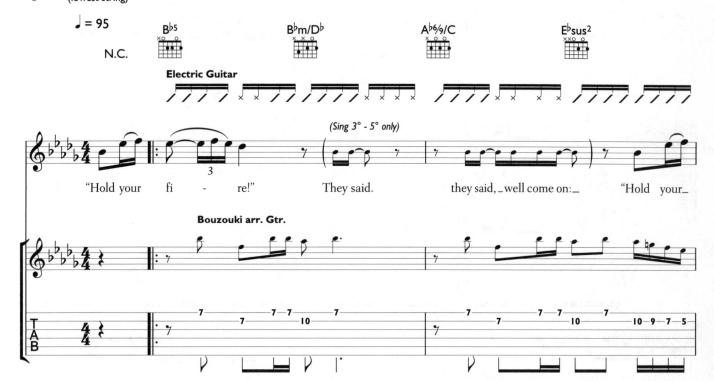

"Hold your fi - re!" They said. they said, well come on: "Hold your

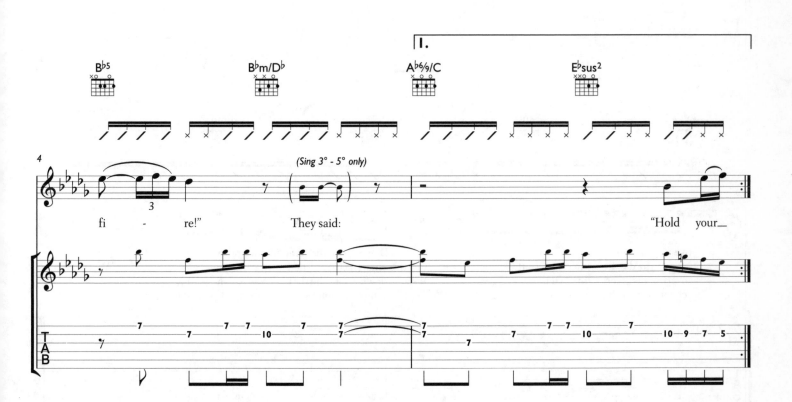

fi - re!" They said: "Hold your

22

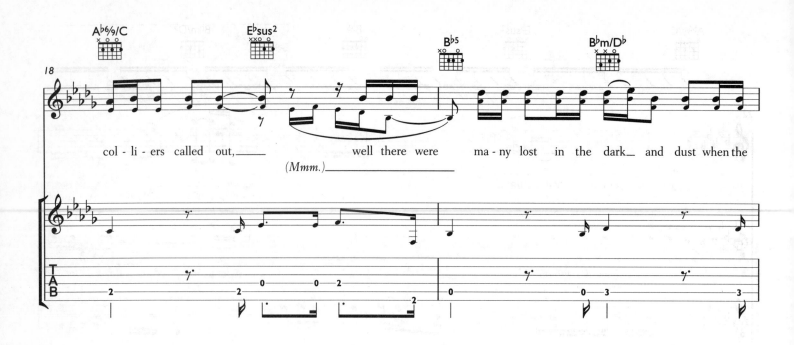

col-li-ers called out,_____ well there were ma-ny lost in the dark_ and dust when the

(Mmm.)_____

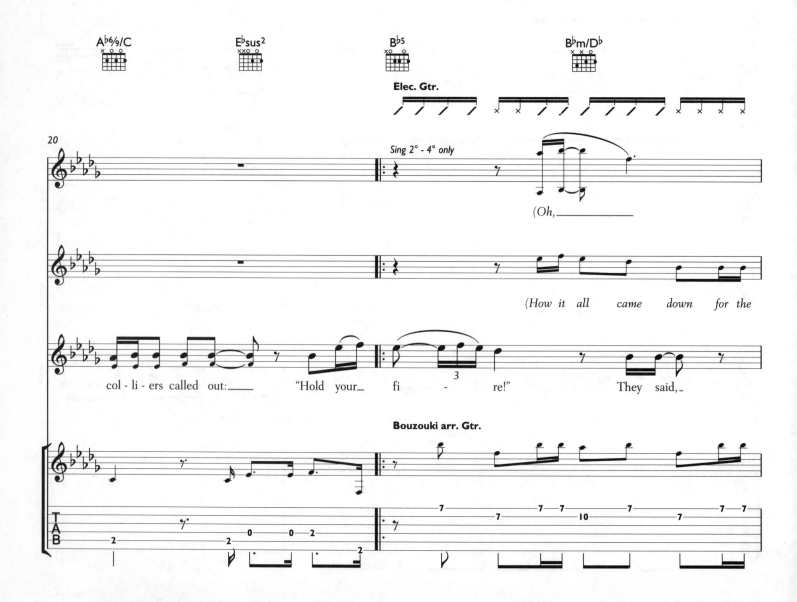

Elec. Gtr.

Sing 2° - 4° only

(Oh,_____

(How it all came down for the

col-li-ers called out:_____ "Hold your_ fi - re!" They said,_

Bouzouki arr. Gtr.

*When her sweetheart is called up to fight in the Great War, a young woman is left to count the days until his return.*

# KING AND COUNTRY

## Words and Music by Seth Lakeman

**Capo 2nd fret**

**Tune guitar:**

① = D ④ = D
② = A ⑤ = A
③ = G ⑥ = D (lowest string)

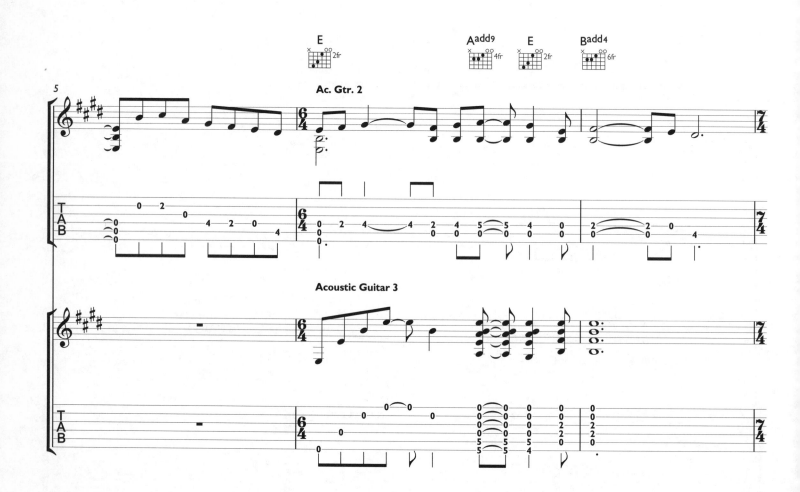

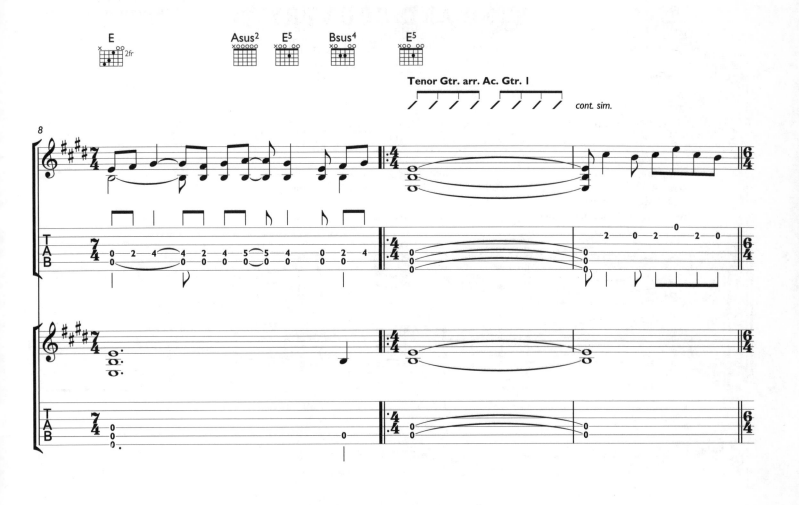

1. Fold - ing hills and a sil - - - ver lane,
2. The first sea - son passed with - out_____ news.
3. The wind blew in a few small drops of_____ rain.
4. Out of the door - way, her hands u - pon_____ her head,

28

# CHILDE THE HUNTER

Words and Music by Seth Lakeman

One of Dartmoor's most enduring legends, Hunter Childe became lost in a blizzard. To save himself from dying of exposure he crawled inside his dead horse and wrote a note passing all his estate to those who would find his body.

34

35

*Tale of two young men and local huntsmen*
*in fast pursuit.*

# TAKE NO ROGUES

## Words and Music by Seth Lakeman

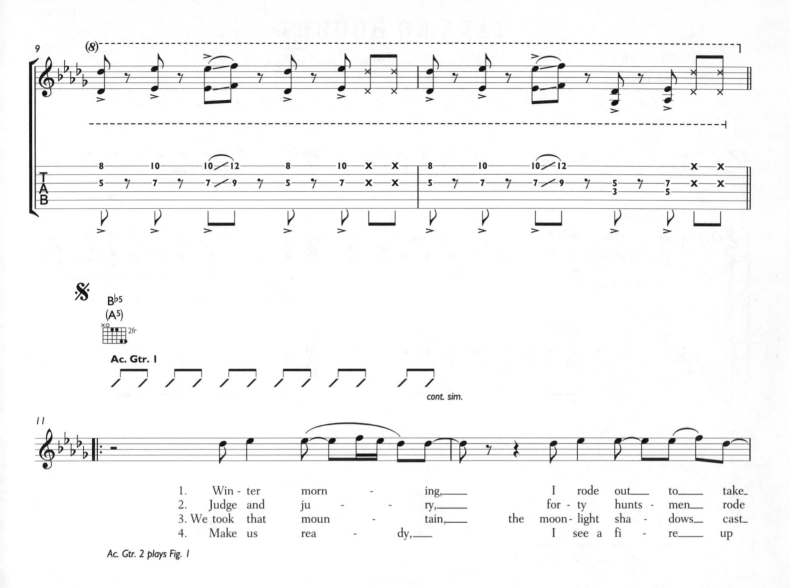

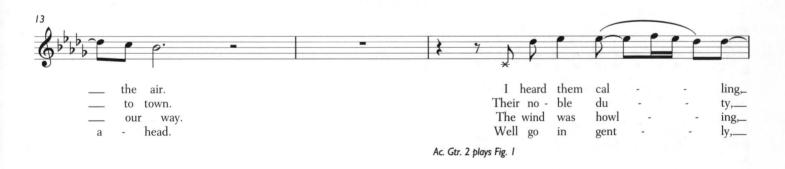

1. Win - ter morn - ing, I rode out to take
2. Judge and ju - ry, for - ty hunts - men rode
3. We took that moun - tain, the moon - light sha - dows cast
4. Make us rea - dy, I see a fi - re up

_Ac. Gtr. 2 plays Fig. 1_

— the air.
— to town.
— our way.
a - head.

I heard them cal - - ling,
Their no - ble du - - ty,
The wind was howl - - ing,
Well go in gent - - ly,

_Ac. Gtr. 2 plays Fig. 1_

— there's a hunt to - day de - clared.
— to track those foot - prints up and down.
— we must catch our bird of prey.
— load those ri - fles up with lead.

40

beau - ty,___ took no gold.   Take no   pri - so - ners,_____ take no

*Acou. Gtr. 2 plays Fig. 2*

*2° - 4° Elec. Gtr. plays Fig. 4*

*Acou. Gtr. 2 plays Fig. 3*

rogues__

**Bouzouki arr. Gtr.**

*Ac. Gtr. 2 plays Fig. 1*

rogues__

**Ac. Gtr. 2**

*Fig. 5*

The Freedom Fields Battle was one of the turning points in the English Civil War. People of Plymouth stood united against the royalists leading to parliament as we know it today.

# 1643

## Words and Music by Seth Lakeman

(1.) this fair town_ we laid__ them down__ in Six-teen For-ty-Three,__ it was
(2.) shot rang out_ from be-hind the hill__ as we marched a-long the bank.__ We were
(3.) night crept in, well the stars__ were dim,__ no sol-dier made a sound.__ We had

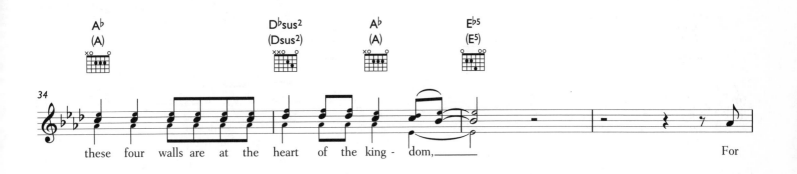

these four walls are at the heart of the king - dom,_____ For

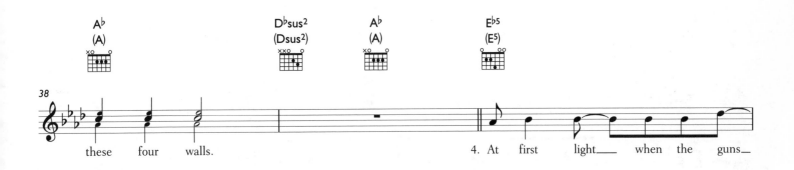

these four walls. 4. At first light___ when the guns___

___ were quiet, re - in - force-ments came___ to town,_____ they were

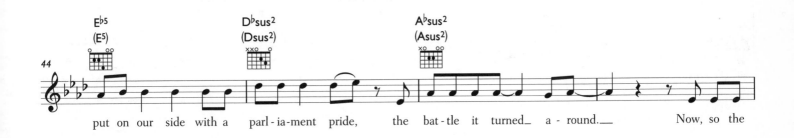

put on our side with a parl - ia-ment pride, the bat-tle it turned___ a - round.___ Now, so the

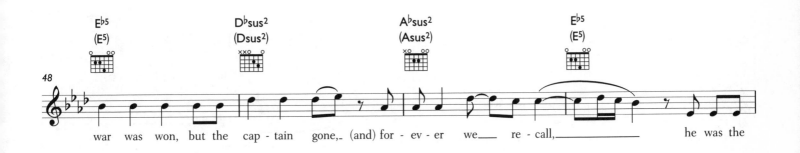

war was won, but the cap - tain gone,___ (and) for - ev - er we___ re - call,_____ he was the

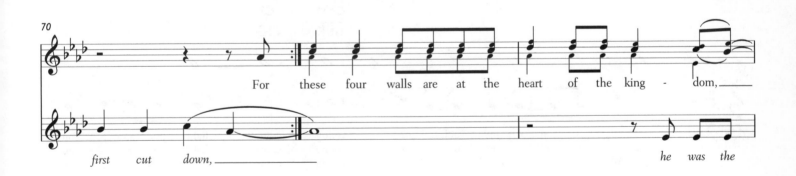

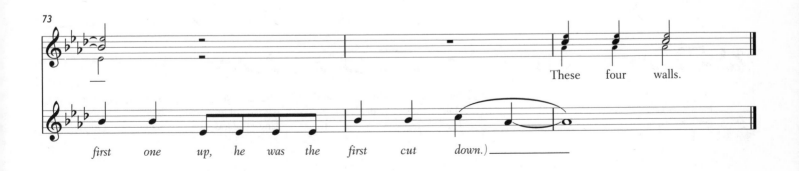

*Inspired by one of the victories during the Anglo-Dutch war in 1653.*

# RIFLEMEN OF WAR

### Words and Music by Seth Lakeman

**Tune guitar:**

① = D  ④ = D
② = B  ⑤ = A
③ = G  ⑥ = D (lowest string)

♩ = 85

*Acoustic Guitar*

Play section x4

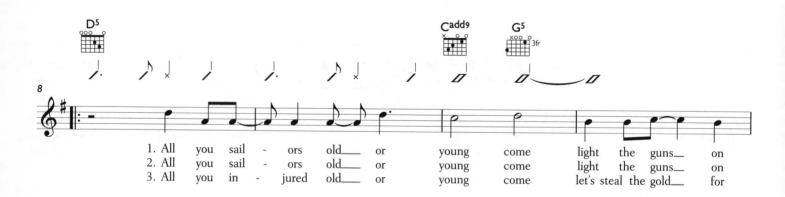

*Violin*

1. All you sail - ors old___ or young come light the guns___ on
2. All you sail - ors old___ or young come light the guns___ on
3. All you in - jured old___ or young come let's steal the gold___ for

ev - 'ry - one.     We'll take the ship___ and off___ to sea, we'll
ev - 'ry - one.     Make that shot___ a - gainst their bow, we
ev - 'ry - one.     Take the ship,___ to Eng - land sail. Good

*A soldier is obsessed by his love —*
*a true charmer.*

# THE CHARMER

## Words and Music by Seth Lakeman

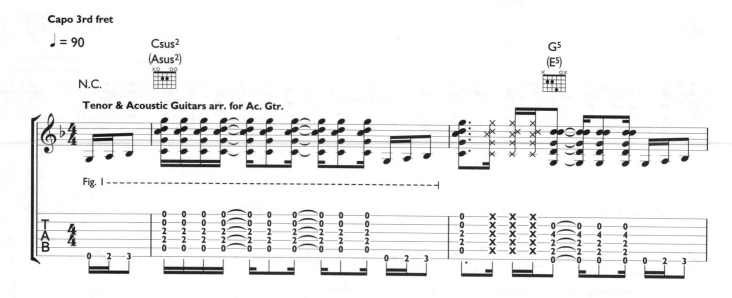

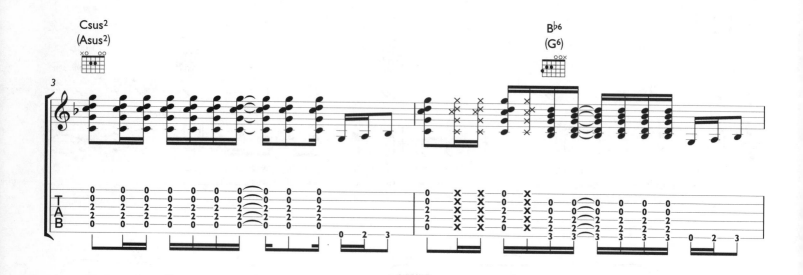

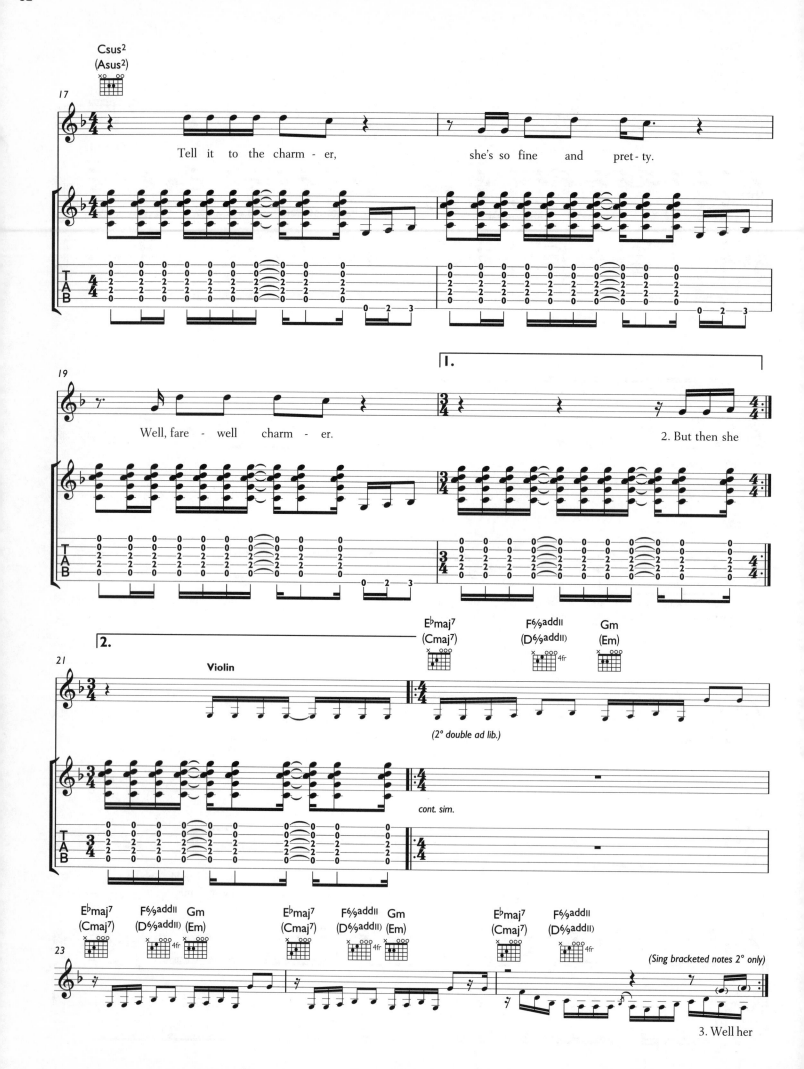

# FINAL LOT

## Words and Music by Seth Lakeman

**Capo 2nd fret**

**Tune guitar:**

① = D  ④ = D
② = A  ⑤ = A
③ = F#  ⑥ = D (lowest string)

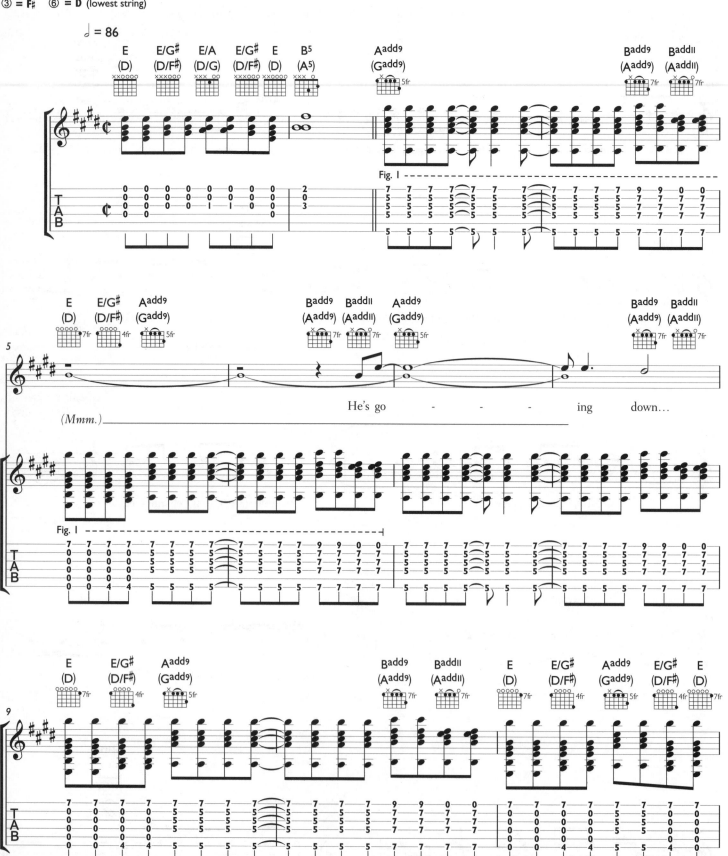

*Promises made by a young couple
and their tokens of gold.*

# BAND OF GOLD

### Words and Music by Seth Lakeman

**Capo 3rd fret**

**Tune guitar:**

① = D    ④ = D
② = B    ⑤ = A
③ = G    ⑥ = E (lowest string)

1. A sum - mer eve - ning, a maid - en fair_____ was
2. The wind is fresh - 'ning up - on her eyes,_____

walk - ing forth in the op - en air._____
down the years that stretch___ so wide._____

(1.) She met her lov - er on the way, she
(2.) Ang - els sing so far a - way, his
(%) 3. A sum - mer eve - ning, a maid - en fair was

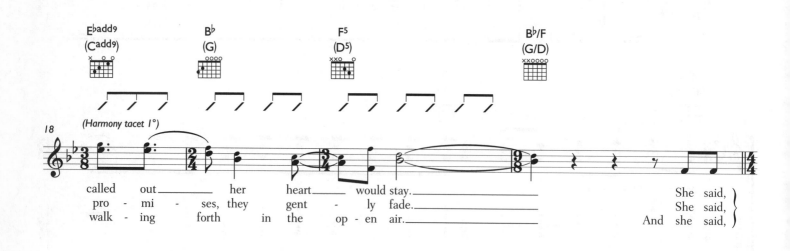

called out her heart would stay. She said,
pro - mi - ses, they gent - ly fade. She said,
walk - ing forth in the op - en air. And she said,

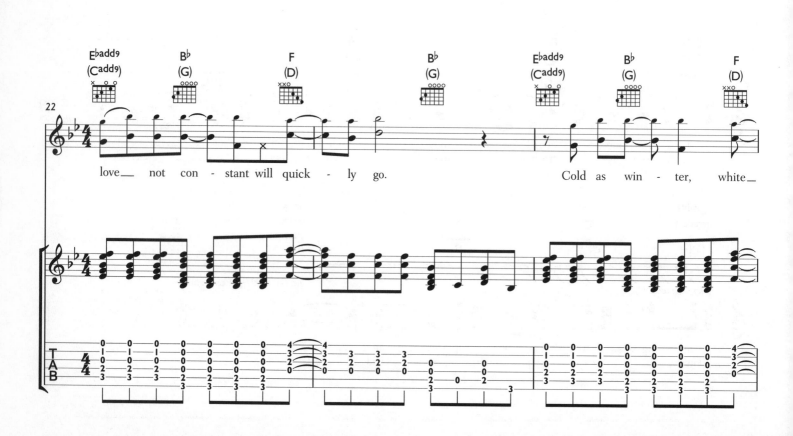

love not con - stant will quick - ly go. Cold as win - ter, white

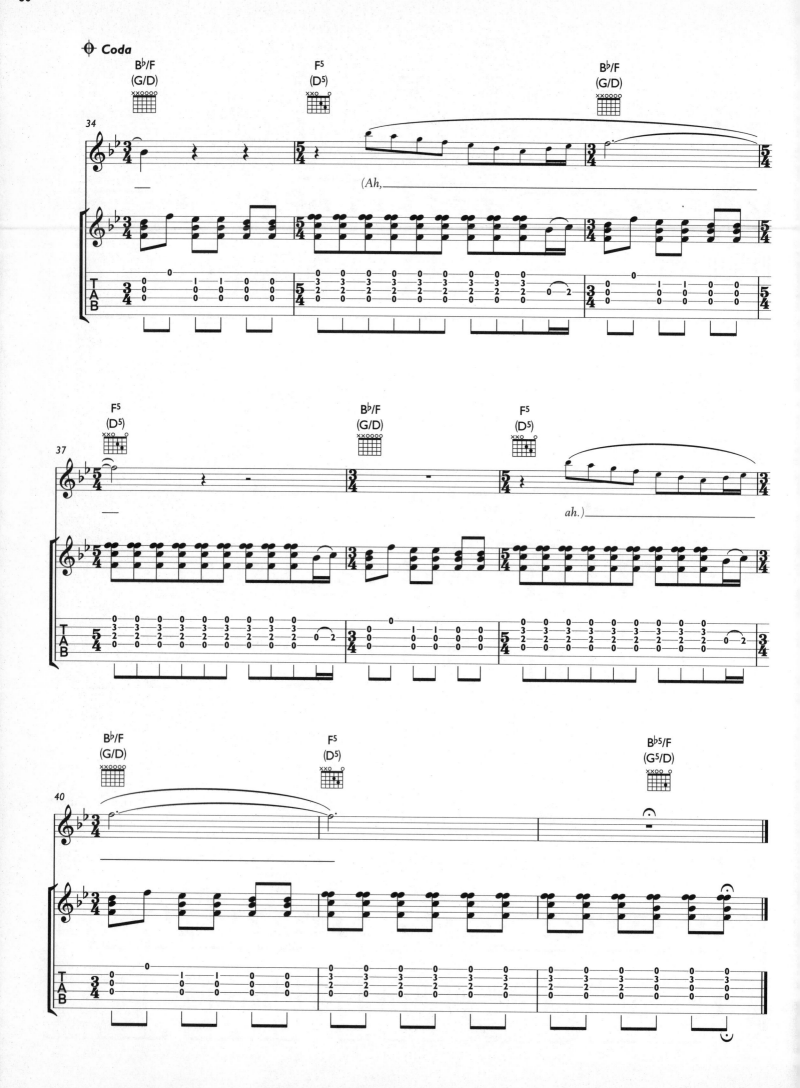

# SEND YOURSELF AWAY

### Words and Music by Seth Lakeman

Tune guitar:
①  = D  ④ = D
②  = A  ⑤ = G
③  = G  ⑥ = D (lowest string)

# Notation and Tablature explained

## Understanding chord boxes

Chord boxes show the neck of your guitar as if viewed head on—the vertical lines represent the strings (low E to high E, from left to right), and the horizontal lines represent the frets.

An **X** above a string means 'don't play this string'.
An **O** above a string means 'play this open string'.
The black dots show you where to put your fingers.

A curved line joining two dots on the fretboard represents a 'barre'. This means that you flatten one of your fingers (usually the first) so that you hold down all the strings between the two dots at the fret marked.

A fret marking at the side of the chord box shows you where chords that are played higher up the neck are located.

## Tuning your guitar

The best way to tune your guitar is to use an electronic tuner. Alternatively, you can use relative tuning; this will ensure that your guitar is in tune with itself, but won't guarantee that you will be in tune with the original track (or any other musicians).

## How to use relative tuning

Fret the low E string at the 5th fret and pluck; compare this with the sound of the open A string. The two notes should be in tune. If not, adjust the tuning of the A string until the two notes match.

Repeat this process for the other strings according to this diagram:

Note that the B string should match the note at the 4th fret of the G string, whereas all the other strings match the note at the 5th fret of the string below.

As a final check, ensure that the bottom E string and top E string are in tune with each other.

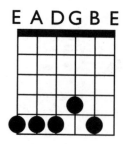

## Detuning and Capo use

If the song uses an unconventional tuning, it will say so clearly at the top of the music, e.g. '6 = D' (tune string 6 to D) or 'detune guitar down by a semitone'. If a capo is used, it will tell you the fret number to which it must be attached. The standard notation will always be in the key at which the song sounds, but the guitar tab will take tuning changes into account. Just detune/add the capo and follow the fret numbers. The chord symbols will show the sounding chord above and the chord you actually play below in brackets.

## Use of figures

In order to make the layout of scores clearer, figures that occur several times in a song will be numbered, e.g. 'Fig. 1', 'Fig. 2', etc. A dotted line underneath shows the extent of the 'figure'. When a phrase is to be played, it will be marked clearly in the score, along with the instrument that should play it.

## Reading Guitar Tab

Guitar tablature illustrates the six strings of the guitar graphically, showing you where you put your fingers for each note or chord. It is always shown with a stave in standard musical notation above it. The guitar tablature stave has six lines, each of them representing a different string. The top line is the high E string, the second line being the B string, and so on. Instead of using note heads, guitar tab uses numbers which show the fret number to be stopped by the left hand. The rhythm is indicated underneath the tab stave. Ex. 1 (below) shows four examples of single notes.

Ex. 2 shows four different chords. The 3rd one (Asus4) should be played as a barre chord at the 5th fret. The 4th chord (C9) is a half, or jazz chord shape. You have to mute the string marked with an 'x' (the A string in this case) with a finger of your fretting hand in order to obtain the correct voicing.

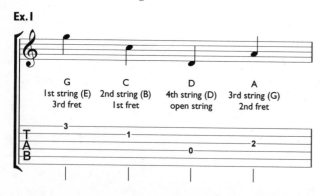

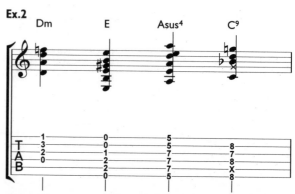

# Notation of other guitar techniques

## Picking hand techniques:

### 1. Down and up strokes
These symbols show that the first and third notes are to be played with a down stroke of the pick and the others up strokes.

### 2. Palm mute
Mute the notes with the palm of the picking hand by lightly touching the strings near the bridge.

### 3. Pick rake
Drag the pick across the indicated strings with a single sweep. The extra pressure will often mute the notes slightly and accentuate the final note.

### 4. Arpeggiated chords
Strum across the indicated strings in the direction of the arrow head of the wavy line.

### 5. Tremolo picking
Shown by the slashes on the stem of the note. Very fast alternate picking. Rapidly and continuously move the pick up and down on each note.

### 6. Pick scrape
Drag the edge of the pick up or down the lower strings to create a scraping sound.

### 7. Right hand tapping
'Tap' onto the note indicated by a '+' with a finger of the picking hand. It is nearly always followed by a pull-off to sound the note fretted below.

### 8. Tap slide
As with tapping, but the tapped note is slid randomly up the fretboard, then pulled off to the following note.

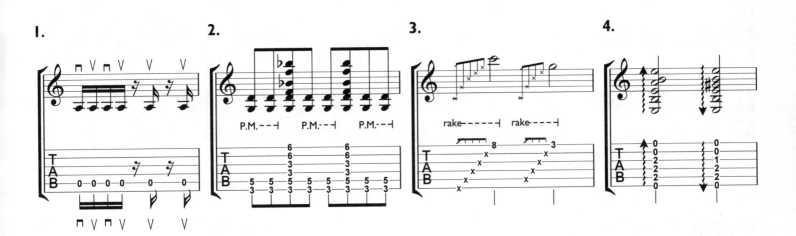

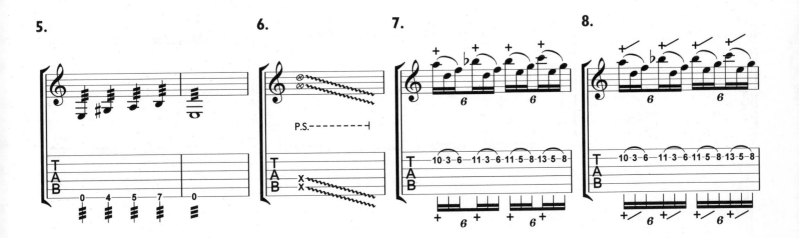

# Fretting hand techniques:

### 1. Hammer-on and pull-off

These consist of two or more notes linked together by a slur. For hammer-ons, fret and play the lowest note, then 'hammer on' to the higher note with another finger. For a pull-off, play the highest note then 'pull off' to a lower note fretted with another finger. In both cases, only pick the first note.

### 2. Glissandi (slides)

Fret and pick the first note, then slide the finger up to the second note. If they are slurred together, do not re-pick the second note.

### 3. Slow glissando

Play the note(s) and slowly slide the finger(s) in the direction of the diagonal line(s).

### 4. Quick glissando

Play the note(s) and immediately slide the finger(s) in the direction of the diagonal line(s).

### 5. Trills

Play the note and rapidly alternate between this note and the nearest one above in the key signature. If a note in brackets is shown before, begin with this note.

### 6. Fret hand muting

Mute the notes with cross noteheads with the fretting hand.

### 7. Left hand tapping

Sound the note by tapping or hammering on to the note indicated by a 'o' with a finger of the fretting hand.

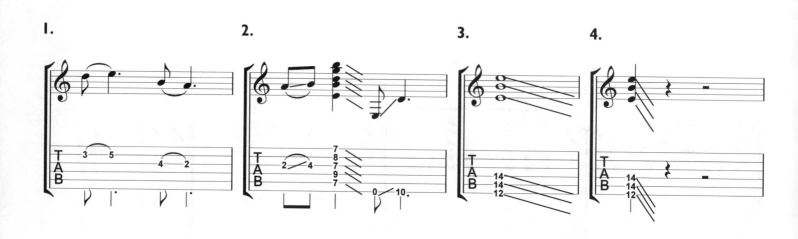

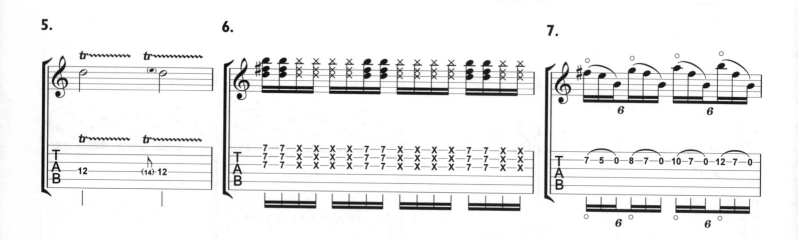

# Bends and vibrato

## Bends

Bends are shown by the curved arrow pointing to a number (in the tab).
Fret the first note and then bend the string up by the amount shown.

### 1. Semitone bend (half step bend)

The smallest conventional interval; equivalent to raising the note by one fret.

### 2. Whole tone bend (whole step bend)

Equivalent to two frets.

### 3. Minor third bend (whole step and a half)

Equivalent to three frets.

### 4. Microtonal bend (quarter-tone bend, Blues curl)

Bend by a slight degree, roughly equivalent to half a fret.

### 5. Bend and release

Fret and pick the first note. Bend up for the length of the note shown. May be followed by a release—letting the string fall back down to the original pitch.

### 6. Ghost bend (prebend)

Fret the bracketed note and bend quickly before picking the note.

### 7. Reverse bend

Fret the bracketed note and bend quickly before picking the note, immediately let fall back to the original.

### 8. Multiple bends

A series of bends and releases joined together. Only pick the first note.

### 9. Unison bend

Strike both indicated notes simultaneously and immediately bend the lower string up to the same pitch as the higher one.

### 10. Double note bend

Play both notes and bend simultaneously by the amount shown.

### 11. Bend involving more than one note

Bend first note and hold the bend whilst striking a note on another string.

### 12. Bends involving stationary notes

Play notes and bend lower string. Hold until release is indicated.

### 13. Vibrato

Shown by a wavy line. The fretting hand creates a vibrato effect using small, rapid up and down bends.

### 14. Bend and tap technique

Play and bend notes as shown, then sound final pitch by tapping onto note as indicated.

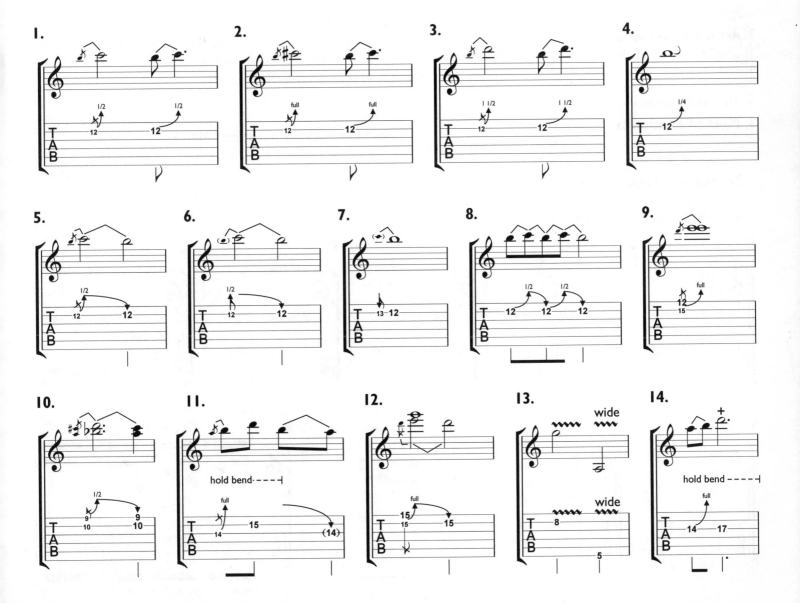

# Tremolo arm (wammy bar)

### 1. Vibrato with tremolo arm
Create vibrato using small, rapid inflections of the tremolo arm.

### 2. Tremolo arm dive and return
Play note and depress tremolo arm by degree shown. Release arm to return to original note.

### 3. Tremolo arm scoop
Depress the arm just before picking the note and release.

### 4. Tremolo arm dip (or doop)
Pick the note, then lower the arm and quickly release.

### 5. Sustained note and dive bomb
Play note, hold for length of time shown and then depress arm to lower the pitch until the strings go slack.

### 6. Gargle
Pick the note and flick the tremolo arm rapidly with the same hand, making the pitch quiver.

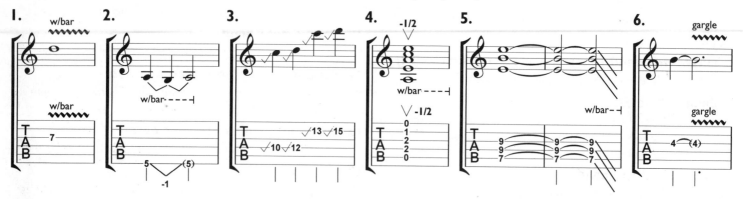

# Harmonics & Other techniques

### 1. Natural harmonics
Instead of fretting properly, touch the string lightly with the fretting hand at the fret shown in the tab. Pick as normal. Diamond noteheads show the resultant pitch.

### 2. Artificial harmonics
The first tab number is fretted and held with the fretting hand as normal. The picking hand then produces a harmonic by using a finger to touch the string lightly at the fret shown by the bracketed number. Pick with another finger of the picking hand.

### 3. Pinched harmonics
Fret the note as shown, but create a harmonic by digging into the string with the side of the thumb as you pick it.

### 4. Tapped harmonics
Fret the note as shown, but create the harmonic through tapping lightly with the picking hand at the fret shown in brackets.

### 5. Touch harmonics
Fret the first note, hold it, then touch the string lightly at the fret shown at the end of the slur with the picking hand.

### 6. Violining
Turn the volume control to zero, pick the notes and then turn the control to fade the note in smoothly.

### 7. Fingering (fretting hand)
Small numbers show the finger with which each note is to be fretted.

### 8. Fingerpicking notation (PIMA)
Notation that shows which finger should be used to pick each note when playing finger style. $p$ = thumb, $i$ = index, $m$ = middle, $a$ = ring.